dreaming

dreaming

★ a countdown to sleep ★

Elaine Greenstein

SCHOLASTIC INC.

New York Toronto London Auckland Sydney
Mexico City New Delhi Hong Kong Buenos Aires

Arthur A. Levine Books hardcover edition designed by Kristina Albertson,
published by Arthur A. Levine Books, an imprint of Scholastic Press, March 2000

ISBN 0-439-06303-5

12 11 10 9 8 7 6 5   7 8 9/0

Printed in the U.S.A.   08

First Scholastic paperback printing, November 2001

The illustrations in this book are monoprints overpainted with gouache.
The text type was set in Mrs. Eaves Bold.

for

motoko

Ten

silent houses,
everyone sleeping

Nine
trees bending
in windy yards

Eight

leaves airborne,

whirling, swirling

Seven
stars, shining
high and low

Six

fish leaping
up to catch them

Five

clouds full

of summer rain

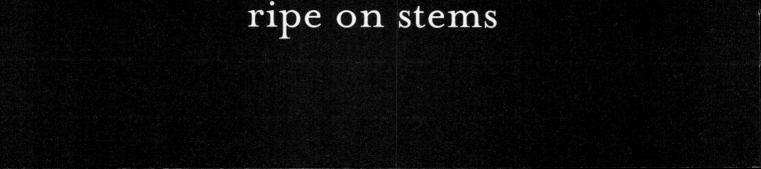

ripe on stems

Three
red foxes,
lapping, sipping

Two

water lilies

floating on ripples

One

lone swan

curling into the moon

Here you are, almost sleeping . . .

Sweet dreams.